A winter coat
For a billy-goat
Or underwear
For a grizzly bear.

A long, long scarf
For a tall giraffe
Or purple pants
For elephants.

Knitting, knitting,
Always knitting –
Grandpa Gitting
Is ALWAYS knitting!

Mark Burgess

3

Out in Space

Nod saw the spaceship come down.

"Here comes Doodle," he said.

"Let's go and see Doodle."

Nod ran to the spaceship.

Wig ran to see Doodle. "We looked for you," she said. "Where did you go?"

"Out in space," said Doodle.

"In space?" asked Nod.

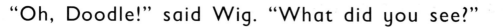

"Oh, Doodle!" said Wig. "What did you see?"

"I saw people," said Doodle.

Nod said, "People! Doodle saw people."

"What are people like?" asked Wig.
"What do they do?"

Doodle said, "People are funny.
They do funny things. They live in boxes."

"Oh, no!" said Wig. "Not in boxes!"

"I saw things that looked like beetles,"
said Doodle.

"Beetles!" said Nod. "Doodle saw beetles."

"Some people ride in beetles," said Doodle.

"Oh, no!" said Wig. "Not in beetles!"

"The beetles have eyes," said Doodle.
"Some eyes are red, and some are yellow."

"Eyes!" said Nod. "Doodle saw beetles with
red and yellow eyes."

Wig said, "I want to go out in space, too.
I want to see all the things you saw, Doodle.
Will you take me?"

"Take me, too," said Nod. "I want to
see people, and boxes, and beetles. Beetles with
red eyes and beetles with yellow eyes."

"Let's go!" said Doodle.
And away they went –

Doodle,

Nod,

and Wig.

Mr Pine's signs

Mr Pine made signs. He made signs that said Stop. He made signs that said Go.

Mr Pine made all the signs in the town.
He made signs for the streets.
He made signs for the buildings.

The people in the town liked the signs that he made. But the signs in the town got old. They got too old for people to read.

The mayor said, "I will ask Mr Pine to make some new signs."
The mayor went to find Mr Pine.

FS/420058

"The signs are too old for people to read.
Will you make new signs for the town?"
asked the mayor.

"Yes, I will," said Mr Pine.
"I can put up the signs, too."

The mayor went home, and Mr Pine set to work.

Mr Pine made red signs, and green signs, and yellow signs.

A yellow sign said Stop. A red sign said Park.

A green sign said Hill Street.

"Now the signs are all made," said Mr Pine.
"I'm tired. I'm going to sleep."

When Mr Pine got up, he said,

"Now, where did I put my glasses?"

He looked and looked.

"I can't find my glasses," he said. "That's funny!

I don't know where they are."

Mr Pine looked here.

And here.

And here.

"I can't stop to find my glasses," said Mr Pine.

"I have to put up the new signs."

He got the signs and went out of the house.

Mr Pine put up all the signs.

He didn't have his glasses so he didn't know

they were mixed up. But they were!

The signs in the street looked funny.

They were all mixed up!

A man said, "What's this?"

A woman said, "Oh, no!"

The policeman said, "Who did this?"

The mayor said, "Find Mr Pine. Quick!"

"All the signs are up," said Mr Pine when
he got home. "Now I can look for my glasses.
Where can they be?"
He looked and looked.
"Did I put them in here?" he said.
He could not find them.

Then Mr Pine looked in the dog kennel.

He said, "My glasses! What are they doing here?"

He put on his glasses and went to see the signs.

This is what Mr Pine saw.

"Oh dear!" said Mr Pine.

"My signs are all mixed up."

"Mr Pine! Mr Pine!" said the mayor.

"Do something! Sort out the signs!"

Mr Pine set to work.

He sorted out all the signs in the town.

Now they are not mixed up.

Old MacDonald

"I want to sleep," said Old MacDonald.

"Go away and let me sleep."

Did the animals go away?

No, they did not.

The goat said, "Ma-a-a!"

The duck said, "Quack! Quack!"

The cow said, "Moo-oo! Moo-oo!"

Old MacDonald said, "I can't sleep here, but
I know what I can do. I'm going to the city."

The animals saw Old MacDonald
go away in his car.

"Ma-a-a! Ma-a-a!" said the goat.
"Quack! Quack!" said the duck.
"Moo-oo! Moo-oo!" said the cow.

Away went Old MacDonald.

"I want to see the new buildings," he said.

"I will walk up and down the streets.

And I will walk in the park.

I'm going to sleep in the city, too."

Old MacDonald saw some new buildings.
He walked up and down the streets, and
he walked in the park.
"Now I want to sleep," said Old MacDonald.
"My animals can't stop me from
sleeping in the city."

Did Old MacDonald go to sleep?

No, he did not.

"Who can sleep in this city?" he asked. "I can't!

Not with cars going up and down the streets.

The cars come and go, and they don't stop."

Old MacDonald said, "I'm going home.

I will get my car and go now."

He walked down the street, and away he went.

Old MacDonald went home and he went to bed.

"I'm going to sleep," he said. "Now!"

The goat said, "Ma-a-a!"

The duck said, "Quack! Quack!"

The cow said, "Moo-oo! Moo-oo!"

Did Old MacDonald get up? No, he did not.

He was so tired that he went to sleep.